# The Art of Manifestation
# Astro-Moon Diary

from the I Choose Love Series.
The Pathway of the Spiritual Warrior.

The Art of Manifestation

Astro-Moon Diary 2020

This Diary Belongs to…

……………………………………………

The Art of Manifestation Astro-Moon Diary
From the I Choose Love Series
The Pathway of the Spiritual Warrior

First Published 2019 A-Z of Emotional Health Ltd.

Published by the A-Z of Emotional Health Ltd.



The intent of the author is only to offer information of a general nature to assist in an individual's search for emotional and spiritual wellness. In the event that you use any of the information in this book for yourself, the author and publisher assume no responsibility for your actions.

# The Art of Manifestation
# Astro-Moon Diary

## Welcome to 2020

## Contents

My deepest respect goes out to you all, for in using books and resources like this, you make a personal choice to walk a conscious path in alignment with the natural energy of the greater universal consciousness of which we are all an integral part.

Namaste

# The Art of Manifestation

The art of manifestation involves not only imagining and dreaming of the kind of life that we wish to have, we must also take actions that enable our dreams to find form. Our state of mind, our attitudes and perceptions, and the way that we feel, our emotions, all have an impact on our ability to fully immerse ourselves in this creative process.

It seems to me that manifestation has its own cyclical pattern.

- We listen to our desires, and we allow ourselves to dream.
- We imagine possibilities and we honor their potential.
- We evaluate and decide what steps we must take to initiate these possibilities into form.
- Remaining open to ongoing evaluation, we commit to a pathway forward.
- We persevere in our doing, trusting that any diversions and interruptions are sent to us to bring greater meaning, clarity and direction.
- When needed, whether in our external actions or deep within our own psyche, we identify any ongoing work that we need to do to keep the energy flowing.
- We continue on our ongoing pathway of evolution and co-creativity, and trust that we will always be shown the next steps.
- Listening to the wisdom and guidance of the universe, when needed we course correct.
- Trusting that the universe knows of our fullest potential and holds a higher vision for us than we ourselves could possibly imagine, we understand that we will be given what we need, although not always necessarily what we want.
- Our pathway emerges and our dreams begin to take form.

# How to Use this Diary

The Art of Manifestation and the Influence of the Moon.

Given that the magnetic pull of the Moon is sufficiently powerful to move our oceans, and that we as human beings are made up of around 70% water, it makes perfect sense to recognize that this powerful magnetic force will have an impact on us all.

Given that our state of mind, our attitudes and perceptions, and the way that we feel, our emotions, all have an impact on our levels of confidence, both in our internal self-belief and in our ability to take real action and 'to do', for anyone who is interested in enhancing their skills of conscious manifestation, it makes even more sense to take some time to understand how this influence affects us each as individuals and to capitalize on these cycles of incoming energy.

In the ocean of our lives, it can be incredibly helpful to know, when to surf the waves, when to tread water or learn to float, when to swim against the tide, or indeed, if we find ourselves in deep water, when to become a diver.

One of the best ways of learning to align and work with the incoming energy of the Moon and her connection with the incoming energy from any of the other planets, is to learn to listen to ourselves and to notice how we find ourselves thinking, feeling and responding to these incoming influences.

To do this, we will need to be aware of where the Moon is during her monthly cycle, along with some awareness of her relationships with the other planets as well.

This diary is designed to help you to do exactly this.

Each month as well as highlighting key phases of the Moon, you will also find further information about the incoming energy and potential influences of some of the other major collaborations and planetary connections.

Alongside the daily calendar dates which can be used as a standard diary, you will also find additional pages for you to journal and record your own experiences.

The more that you do this, the more you will be able to recognize the way in which these influences affect you in a personal way, allowing you to understand and work with the incoming energy on an ongoing basis, finetuning your ability to become consciously co-creative on your personal journey of manifestation.

### The Phases of the Moon, the Influence of the Zodiac, Lunar and Solar Eclipses and the Retrograde Planets.

At the beginning of this book you will find information about the different phases of the moon and the way that you can use and understand these natural cycles as part of the process of manifestation, including the impact of both solar and lunar eclipses, plus a description of the way that the lunar energy is affected and channeled as the moon travels through each sign of the zodiac. I have also explained the potential impact of the influences of Mercury, Venus and Mars in retrograde, and listed the dates that these events occur.

### The Turning of the Seasons, the Solstices and Equinoxes.

For thousands of years the wisdom traditions have marked and celebrated the changing of the seasons honoring and appreciating the shifts in energy that take place during these times and so I have also shared some thoughts about the solstices and the equinoxes and the way in which we can utilize the energy of these pivotal moments of natural transition to support us in becoming consciously co-creative.

By recording your own experiences, as you journey through the year, this diary will form a personal record for you to continue to build upon and deepen your understanding of how to align yourself with the natural rhythms of the this extraordinary planet and her relationship with the energy of the planets that surround us.

The times given on the daily diary pages are in GMT. Use the time differences below to reference the Moons influence to your own location.

| | |
|---|---|
| Central Europe | +1hr |
| Eastern Europe | +2hrs |
| India | +5.30hrs |
| Australia | +8hrs |
| New Zealand | +12hrs |
| USA EST | -5hrs |
| USA CST | -6hrs |
| USA MST | -7hrs |
| USA PST | -8hrs |

# The Phases of the Moon

The New Moon.

The new moon is traditionally associated with the setting of intentions and so the energy at this time naturally invites us to meditate into a space of possibility. If you are a daily meditator, you may already find that for the two days before and the two days after the new moon, your mind may be inclined to wander during your meditations.

If this is the case you may find it helpful to have a pen and paper close by, or use the journaling pages in this diary to make a note of any ideas that come to you during your meditation practice. Personally, during this phase of the moon, I find myself naturally drawn to walking meditations.

Consciously make the effort to spend time outdoors and immerse yourself in nature and whatever your preferred way of finding stillness, calm your mind, and enter your own dreamtime. Let your mind wander into the depths of the new moon energy and give yourself permission to dream big!

The Crescent Moon.

In the phase of the crescent moon the seeds that emerged at the new moon will begin to whisper to you, calling to be heard. How we respond to this inner calling will have a direct influence on our ability to be proactive in our developing process of manifestation.

Take your yearnings and your desires seriously and notice any thinking patterns that may be holding you back or limiting your perspectives. In the process of manifestation, we are both doers and deciders and so the extent of our external manifestations will always be a reflection of our ability to embrace our inner growth. At this time, any resistance to change can be identified, paving the way for this month's cycle of inner growth.

The crescent moon invites us to identify any resistances within us, any patterns of thinking or self-sabotaging attitudes and behaviors that may limit us from stepping into the fullest potential of our dreams. Our very recognition of these patterns will automatically diminish their power as well as opening up opportunities and avenues of potential healing and resolution.
The First Quarter Moon.

The first quarter moon is sometimes thought of as a time when hurdles and obstacles that need to be overcome, will push forwards and enter into our awareness. Personally, I have found that the energy of the first quarter moon affects me in a far more vibrant and positive way.

During this phase of the moon, having identified any inner blocks to progress, during the crescent moon, the seeds of ideas that were planted at the new moon, push themselves forwards in abundance, and I find myself flooded with thoughts of what I will need to do to nurture the possibilities of the new moon, to enable them to begin to take shape and manifest into real form.

I look carefully at the scope of my ideas and begin to focus on those which are most important for me to initiate at this moment in time. The combination of the seeds of the new moon and the learning discovered at the crescent moon, enables me to prioritize and to formulate my actions for the coming month.

## The Gibbous Moon.

In the time of the gibbous moon energy is building, passions are high, and dreams are calling to be made real. Ideas begin to take shape, and the pathway forward gains clarity. Taking time to hold my intentions and my vision for the future in mind, I ground myself in the present moment, and I request guidance in knowing which steps to take in the here and now, before turning my decisions into acts of doing.

Take time to celebrate the joy to be found in the excitement of anticipation, whilst remaining present and grounded. Hold your vision but treasure the here and now moments of your journey and be available to receive guidance. Stay on track, but simultaneously be open to any course corrections that you are guided towards.

## The Full Moon.

The power and energy of the full moon is extraordinary. For anyone who works with healing stones and crystals, be sure to place them outside overnight to recharge in the eliminating power of the full moon. Their energy of release and repair will be revitalized for any healing work over the coming month.

The full brightness of this powerful and highly charged energy brings a space of authenticity where all is revealed and illuminated, and so the full moon is often a time when we experience heightened and intense emotions.

Be kind to yourself and others. Notice and listen, particularly to any situations that are not okay. Things that are usually tolerated or brushed under the carpet will surface and request your attention. So, if you find yourself experiencing any challenging emotions please take them seriously.

The energy of this phase of the moon brings a wonderful opportunity to notice, to listen, to reflect, and then to release and let go, clearing the way to move forwards.

In the process of manifestation, if we find ourselves unable to move forwards or feel stuck in some way, it is often some aspect of our past that is still lingering, blocking us from believing in ourselves or believing in others or finding trust in the possibility of a different future. Anyone who has ever experienced trauma or abuse will tell you that whilst the physical scars will heal, it is the emotional ones that remain.

The full moon illuminates our emotions highlighting exactly what is working for us... as well as anything that is not!

Learn to differentiate between emotions that connect to past experiences, as opposed to emotions that are part of your immediate response system helping you to navigate your life in the here and now. There is a difference!

Our emotions contain and generate energy. Understanding this difference between past and present emotional influences allows you to identify anything that you need to release from the past, empowering you to channel any highly charged emotional energy into positive action.

If you find yourself struggling with challenging emotional states, you may find 'Mindfulness Meets Emotional Awareness - 7 steps to learn the language of your emotions' a useful read. This book explains exactly how and why our most challenging emotions serve us and will teach you how to transform and channel any highly charged emotions into actions that support your pathway rather than hinder it.

### The Disseminating Moon.

As the energy of the full moon diminishes, emotions are released, and forgiveness is discovered. This phase of the moon brings opportunity to step into a position of authentic empowerment. Within this energetic space of emergence, we hold awareness of ourselves, of others and in alignment with the collective soul of humanity, the disseminating Moon invites us to be all that we can be.

This is a time to acknowledge and validate the extraordinariness of who you are, and of everything, both good and bad, that has led you to the place that you stand today and contributed to the person that you are.

Be steady in your actions and in your doings. Stand in your power and be your true self with joy, gratitude and humility. Let the energy of the disseminating moon filter into every cell of your body, affirming your dedication to your pathway.

## The Last Quarter Moon.

The energy of the last quarter moon invites us to walk our talk. If the full moon energy gives us an opportunity to upgrade our system, letting go of anything that no longer serves us, then the last quarter moon is a time that invites us to integrate our learning and to follow it through in all that we do and in all that we are.

The energy of this moon brings us the opportunity to make sure that our plans, actions and decisions are congruent with all that we wish to be and all that we wish to see in the world.

Stand firm and pay attention to the details of your world and notice if any adjustments need to be made. From a spiritual perspective, do you need to cross any T's or dot any I's to ensure that in all areas of your life, you are living in congruence with your truest values and deepest desires. Within the unique circumstances of your own process of co-creativity are you 'being' everything that you wish to attract for yourself.

For example, how positive are your thoughts? Does your inner critic offer constructive feedback or harsh criticism? Are you kinder to others than to yourself? ...or is it the other way around?

Centre yourself in compassion, kindness, and above all... in love.

## The Balsamic Moon.

The balsamic Moon asks you to trust. Hold your vision, and yet simultaneously let go of any attachment to specific outcomes. This is a time of preparation and nurture, a time to fertilize the ground in anticipation of the coming new moon and of any new seeds that you may wish to sow.

Keep your energy clean and be particularly aware of your personal energetic resonance. Self-responsibility can be understood to mean 'our ability to be responsive to ourselves'. From an energetic perspective, be sure to cleanse yourself of anything that clings and that may no longer be serving you. Centre yourself in the knowledge that as this monthly lunar phase comes to its completion, you can engage in preparing the ground for your own deliverance, making space within for the emergence of a new cycle of opportunity.

Validate, acknowledge and cherish all that you have achieved during this last phase of manifestation, and in your reflections, remember that there is no wrong way. Anything that appears to have been a wrong turn or a mistake will have led you to exactly the place that you need to be, right now, bringing you the awareness that you needed to take fresh new steps as we approach the coming energy of the next new moon.

# Void of Course Moon

As the moon travels around the earth, it appears to us as if she passes through each of the 12 signs of the zodiac. Sometimes she will move directly from one sign to another, but at other times there is a space in between. This can last just a few minutes, or sometimes several hours. When the moon is 'void of course', it means that she is transitioning through this space, in between two different signs.

As she travels through each sign of the Zodiac the powerful magnetism of her energy is channeled through the energetic resonance or personality of that sign. However, when she is void of course, there is a kind of energetic pause where her energy is no longer guided and therefore manifesting through the influence of a particular sign.

I have noticed that this space of 'in betweenness' affects people in very different and uniquely individual ways, depending on how they are feeling and what is taking place in the immediacy of their lives at any given time.

For some, this pause in the incoming energy of our beloved moon, brings opportunity to be still and to release any goal driven targets, creating a natural channel for insights and illuminations to flow through. However, for others, particularly during periods of extreme change and transition, the void of course moon can feel quite emotionally intense.

At some point in our lives, we will all experience challenging situations and circumstances, this is simply a part of our human journey. Indeed it is often through periods of adversity that we find our greatest learning. But this doesn't mean it's easy! At times of difficulty during our lives, we will inevitably experience some pretty intense emotions and when the moon is void of course it can seem as though emotions are flooding in with no channel to direct or contain them.

In my experience it can pay dividends to notice how the void moon affects us and therefore to anticipate ahead of time how best to use this time. When life is running smoothly, we can actively anticipate using this time for periods of meditation, creating space and availability to receive insights and illumination. However, if life is not running smoothly, we can also actively anticipate using this time appropriately and we can become more consciously attentive in managing our diaries.

There will always be times when the incoming energy will support us in taking action and moving forwards, as well as times when it is more appropriate to hold back, to rest and to pause. Our awareness of the influences and impact of the incoming energy of the moon and other planetary influences and the way that these affect us in a personal way enables us to become conscious in our decision-making and is therefore a valuable skill in the art of manifestation.

## The Moon in the Zodiac Signs

Moon in Aries.

At this emotionally powerful time, use the energy to be assertive and to initiate your ideas. Say how it is and take action.

Moon in Taurus.

Grounded, sensual and earthy, use this energy to attune yourself with the natural rhythms of nature. A great time for walking meditations.

Moon in Gemini.

A time of communication, reaching out and connecting with others, use this energy for networking and socializing.

Moon in Cancer.

A wonderful time to be at home, share food and be in the company of family and close friends. Use this energy to nourish your soul, spending time with those you love.

Moon in Leo.

Sing, laugh, express yourself and find your voice. Use this energy to feel alive and embrace the joy of self-discovery and self-expression. We are never too old to play!

Moon in Virgo.

This energy supports us in attending to any work that requires dedication, structure, order and precision. Approach your tasks with willingness and a desire to serve.

Moon in Libra.

The energy of this moon calls us to seek harmony and to find balance. This is a time to share and to discover ourselves through our relationships and the company of others.

Moon in Scorpio.

A time to journey inwards, this energy connects us to the depths of our unconscious and can bring deep emotions to the surface. Be sure to listen to yourself and take your yearnings seriously.

Moon in Sagittarius.

The energy of this moon invites us to vision in an optimistic future, full of hope and possibility. A great time to expand our horizons and dream big!

Moon in Capricorn.

The energy of this moon invites us to take pragmatic, practical actions to manifest our ideas into form. Get building and embrace the joy of doing.

Moon in Aquarius.

A time to collaborate, share ideas and work together. The energy of this moon invites you to align your individual contribution with a higher vision of greater purpose that will also serve the collective Soul of humanity.

Moon in Pisces.

A time to dream and a time to heal. Open yourself to divine inspiration and allow yourself to be guided. The energy of this moon brings illumination, fuelling imagination and creativity.

# Solar and Lunar Eclipses

During eclipse season, the already intense energy of both the new and full moons are intensified. An eclipse in your sign, will always be a significant trigger point or turning point in your own personal process of evolution and can often herald random events that create sudden and unexpected changes.

On your personal journey of manifestation, understanding this heightened and intensified energy can be incredibly helpful in knowing, when to reflect and set your intentions, and when to take action to move something forwards, particularly if you intend to make or initiate significant changes in any aspect of your life.

Eclipses are also associated with our Karmic journey, creating an energetic rift that overrides our usual perception and connection to time. The energy of the eclipses is said to open an energetic portal that assists us in connecting with our purpose and calling in this present lifetime.

Symbolized in the tarot pack by the cards of Death and the Tower, the energy of both the solar and lunar eclipses are associated with transformation, either internally or in the circumstances of our external lives, and often involves both endings and new beginnings.

When we learn to work with the influence of the eclipses, rather than trying to control events, we consciously make time to allow the energy of a greater universal consciousness to flow through us, bringing us the guidance that we need to support the evolution of our Soul within our human experience.

## Solar Eclipse.

A solar eclipse is when the moon sits in between the sun and the earth, with the moon covering the sun. This will always occur at a new moon. The energy associated with this time is the same as a new moon, but intensified, like a new moon on steroids!

This is the perfect time to get still and to meditate into a space of personal dreamtime and allow your ideas to flow.

The energy of the solar eclipse can bring an extraordinary surge of creative possibilities, although these may not always arrive in the shape or form that we expect. If you are already involved in setting intentions, but then find that something happens to suddenly create a shift in your direction, trust that this unexpected change is important to your personal growth and evolution, and connected to the calling of your soul.

In matters of manifestation, the universe will always have the upper hand and tends to bring us what we need... although not always what we want!

When we can allow ourselves to trust that even in moments of upheaval and disruption we are being gifted with an opportunity, we open ourselves to receive the fullest potential and the greatest learning to be found in every situation.

### Lunar Eclipse.

A lunar eclipse is when the earth sits between the moon and the sun, and this will always occur at a full moon. Full moons are associated with heightened emotions and during a lunar eclipse, emotions can run high, like a full moon on steroids!

If we think of the moon as our Feminine Guardian who circles our planet, gathering the energy of the sun and redistributing it to the earth in various measures, at the time of a Lunar Eclipse, the energy of the moon is like a fully charged battery, highly charged and ready to ignite change.

In the full illumination of the moon at her most powerful, all is revealed. Anything and everything that is running smoothly and working in service of a balanced and authentic life will be apparent to us, confirming that we are walking the right path. Likewise, anything and everything that is not working for us or no longer serves us, both internally and externally, will also be brought into the light, calling to be addressed, changed, and if necessary released.

As long as something remains hidden or unconscious, we are helpless to address the issue and to take actions of resolution, however, when we identify a problem, the very fact that we can see the issue clearly creates an opportunity to seek solutions and find ways forward. On our personal journey of manifestation, the energy of a lunar eclipse increases our connections with any emotional residue from the past that may be clinging and coloring our perspectives inappropriately, creating an amazing opportunity for cleansing and release, clearing the way for resolution and healing. This is a powerful time to embrace forgiveness, of both ourselves and others.

Lunar eclipses are often associated with external changes that are a mirror or a reflection of our internal growth and learning. Whatever is taking place around you, if something in your life appears to be needing to change or to leave, let go gracefully and know that it is timely to the evolution of your soul.

If you are naturally a highly empathic person and particularly sensitive to the feelings of others, at the time of a lunar eclipse you may find yourself highly absorbent to the emotional states of the people around you. Be sure to cleanse and do a daily release ceremony to let go of anything that doesn't belong to you before meditating into your own space of illumination.

- 10-11 January – Full Moon Eclipse in Cancer.
- 5-6 June – Full Moon Eclipse in Sagittarius.
- 20-21 June – New Moon Eclipse in Cancer… and the Solstice!
- 4-5 July – Full Moon Eclipse in Capricorn.
- 30 November – Full Moon Eclipse in Gemini.
- 14-15 December – New moon Eclipse in Sagittarius.

# Mercury, Mars and Venus in Retrograde

Mercury in Retrograde.

- 17th February – 10th March.
- 18th June - 12th July.
- 14th October – 3rd November.

The energy of Mercury in retrograde is often associated with obstructions and delays, and in our target and goal orientated culture, we understandably tend to experience this period through a negative lens. Mercury retrograde periods seem to cause us no end of disruption, our plans go astray, we experience roadblocks and diversions, and there are often difficulties with our IT and communication systems.

However, if we step away from this viewpoint and consider that all aspects of planetary influences can support us and bring us valuable and necessary gifts, this shift in our perspective enables us to stand back and work with the incoming energy.

If there is a diversion, then the universe may be giving you a sign, perhaps you are meant to take an alternative route where you will discover something that was absolutely essential to your personal growth and evolution.

If something from your past raises its head during a Mercury retrograde period, then your attention is required. This is an invitation for you to acknowledge this issue and take time to embark on the necessary steps to lay it to rest.

There will always be times in our lives when the energy is with us to set targets and remain fixed on our course, to plough forwards and to push and to strive, however, given that the energy of Mercury represents our capacity to develop and integrate wisdom on our souls' journey within the human experience, when the Winged Messenger of the Gods temporarily stands still in the heavens and appears to travel backwards, this energy calls us back and asks us to slow down, to take our time and to be alert to any signals and signs that the universe is trying to show us.

Venus in Retrograde.

- 13th May – 25th June.

Are you in balance? Do you allow yourself to receive as much as you give and vice versa? Are you actively involved in your own self-care? Do you pause to celebrate your achievements along the way, and do you give yourself an appropriate amount of time out to relax?

Self-care is not an act of selfishness; it is an act of consciousness.

When Venus moves into retrograde the energy of the feminine invites you to listen to your heart, to override the demands of a busy mind and be centered in your truest values, including and especially your own self-care.

Venus is in retrograde is a wonderful time to reflect and to realign and rebalance all areas of your life. This revitalizing influence of this phase will keep your energy clean and flowing and ensure that your energetic resonance is congruent with all that you wish to manifest into the world. As such, Venus in retrograde plays an essential role in our ability to manifest our truest desires.

During periods of transition, if you have ever found yourself questioning what your true calling might be, when Venus is in retrograde, ask for guidance and be open to receive.

If during this time you find yourself called to stand up for your values, the female warrior energy of Venus will support you in connecting with the lioness within. In the name of kindness, compassion and peace, her retrograde energy will encourage you to find your authentic voice, speak the truth, and stand firm in your boundaries.

Mars in Retrograde.

- 9th September – 14th November.

When we receive the influence of the wonderful, dynamic, forward thrusting momentum of Mars, we often experience high levels of energy, powering us up and enabling us to take actions that move our lives forwards.

But... even warriors need to rest!

When Mars, the masculine warrior planet, pauses and appears to travel backwards, we are invited to slow down, stand back and to gain a perspective of the bigger picture.
Use this wonderful energy of passion and desire to celebrate where you are right now and give yourself time to focus on future plans and the development of strategies before preparing to move ahead again.

Hindsight truly is a wonderful thing! It enables us to learn from our past experiences, to think before we speak, and indeed to think before we take action. Mars in retrograde invites us to integrate the learning from our experiences into our bank of wisdom, ensuring that our passions and desires manifest into choices, decisions and actions inspired by integrity.

Sometimes, during the mars retrograde period, you may be called to stand your ground over an issue of justice and integrity. Be mindful to think before you speak. Channel your passions and your sense of justice through the lens of compassion. Use this time for evaluation and non-judgmental appraisal whilst simultaneously holding firm to your core inner values.

# The Solstices and Equinoxes

At these pivotal moments in the natural cycles of time, it is as though the energy of the Earth pauses for breath. It is as though the space between heaven and earth becomes fluid, translucent and free of clutter. These shifts in time and space offer an extraordinary opportunity to achieve and access higher levels of consciousness and awareness.

During the four days either side of these powerful shifts we can often receive profound downloads of illumination, leading to an increase in our intuitive abilities, heightening our ability to channel and connect with source energy, divine inspiration and with the greater consciousness.

These pivotal moments in time bring extraordinary opportunities to reach a higher vision or viewpoint that can change our perceptions and perspectives, freeing us from limiting beliefs and bringing clarity of mind and new direction.

These periods are the perfect opportunity to engage in any spiritual practice that supports your personal growth and awareness and offer the ideal time to create ceremonies of appreciation, gratitude and celebration, as part of your manifestation process.

As well as the Solstices and the Equinoxes, during the year there are four other pivotal turning points which were understood and celebrated in the Celtic and Pagan traditions. Exactly the same energetic principles apply and depending on whether you are in the northern or southern hemisphere, your ceremonies and celebrations at this time will vary, tuning you to the rhythm of the seasons of your own geographical area.

During these pivotal moments, use this diary to check in with the incoming astrological energy, and allow yourself the time to meditate and take full advantage of the intensified energetic possibilities to enhance your personal process of manifestation.

These key dates are listed below;

- 2nd Feb - Northern Hemisphere Imbolc – Sothern Hemisphere Lammas
- 20th March – Northern Hemisphere Spring Equinox – Southern Hemisphere Autumn Equinox
- 1st May - Northern Hemisphere Beltane – Southern Hemisphere Samhain

- 20th/21st June - Northern Hemisphere Summer Solstice - Southern Hemisphere Winter Solstice
- 2nd/3rd August - Northern Hemisphere Lammas – Southern Hemisphere Imbolc
- 22nd/23rd September -- Northern Hemisphere Autumn Equinox – Southern Hemisphere Spring Equinox
- 31st October - Northern Hemisphere Samhain – Southern Hemisphere Beltane
- 21st December -- Northern Hemisphere Winter Solstice – Southern Hemisphere Summer Solstice

The Art of Manifestation
Astro-Moon Diary

Weekly Diary with Journaling Pages

---------------------------------------------- Journaling & Notes ----------------------------------------------

Journaling & Notes

# Welcome to January 2020

## The Cards this Month

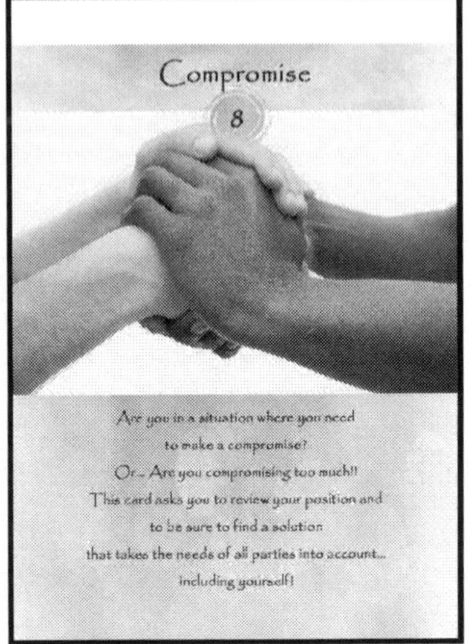

### 7th January - Saturn conjunct Pluto

Welcome to January, and wow, what an energetic and dynamic start to the year! The Saturn and Pluto collaboration that has dominated the energetic scene for most of 2019, calling us to restructure and regenerate anything that no longer serves, will finally come together on the 7th of this month.

The Rune that I was drawn to for this month is Raido, the rune of Journey. This rune speaks of communication, union and re-union and refers to an inner journey to bring about self-healing and self-change. Gently identify and remove any resistances within, clearing the way to connect with your highest vision.

### 10th January - Full Moon Cancer - Lunar Eclipse

The energy of a full moon always speaks of highly charged emotions and a lunar eclipse intensifies and ignites this energy. Add to this the wonderfully compassionate, deeply empathic and emotional personality of cancer and we can begin to anticipate the flavor and emotional depth of the energy we might be experiencing during this month.

A moon of nurture, this is a perfect time to highlight and identify the importance of self-care and to release any limiting beliefs that block our ability to nurture ourselves. Remember, self-care is not an act of selfishness, it is an act of consciousness!

### 24th January – New Moon Aquarius

As the month progresses and we entered the phase of the new Moon, the incoming energy offers us an extraordinary opportunity to integrate the emotional awareness of the full moon eclipse into higher levels of consciousness.

With connections between the Moon, Venus and Neptune and the dynamic and passionate warrior energy of Mars this is the perfect time to set intentions that align our personal passions with a higher vision.

In terms of manifestation, this is the perfect month to practice mindfulness and to integrate, reflective thinking with emotional awareness, both key skills in our ability to move beyond any limiting beliefs that have previously held us back and inhibited us from stepping into our fullest potential.

December 2019 / January 2020

--------------------------------------------- Journaling & Notes ---------------------------------------------

# December 2019 / January 2020

## 30 Monday

Moon in Aquarius - V/C 10.25 – Pisces 15.41

## 31 Tuesday

Moon in Pisces

## 1 Wednesday

Moon in Pisces – New Year's Day

## 2 Thursday

Moon in Pisces – V/C 02.13 – Aries 04.00

## 3 Friday

Moon in Aries – First Quarter Moon 04.45

## 4 Saturday

Moon in Aries – V/C 01.18 – Taurus 16.15

## 5 Sunday

Moon in Taurus

January 2020

Journaling & Notes

## 6 Monday

Moon in Taurus – V/C 12.07

## 7 Tuesday

Moon in Gemini – 02.10

## 8 Wednesday

Moon in Gemini – V/C 22.15

## 9 Thursday

Moon in Cancer – 08.43

## 10 Friday

Moon in Cancer – Full Moon Eclipse 19.21 – V/C 23.58

## 11 Saturday

Moon in Leo 12.15

## 12 Sunday

Moon in Leo

January 2020

Journaling & Notes

## 13 Monday

Moon in Leo – V/C 13.41 – Virgo 14.06

## 14 Tuesday

Moon in Virgo

## 15 Wednesday

Moon in Virgo – V/C 12.11 – Libra 15.43

## 16 Thursday

Moon in Libra

## 17 Friday

Moon in Libra – V/C 12.58 – Scorpio 18.20 – Last Quarter Moon

## 18 Saturday

Moon in Scorpio

## 19 Sunday

Moon in Scorpio – V/C 21.21 – Sagittarius 22.40

January 2020

------------------------------------------------ Journaling & Notes ------------------------------------------------

## 20 Monday

Moon in Sagittarius – Sun enters Aquarius 14.54

## 21 Tuesday

Moon in Sagittarius – V/C 04.45

## 22 Wednesday

Moon in Capricorn 04.59

## 23 Thursday

Moon in Capricorn

## 24 Friday

Moon in Capricorn – V/C 02.08 – Aquarius 13.20 – New Moon Aquarius 21.41

## 25 Saturday

Moon in Aquarius – V/C 19.06

## 26 Sunday

Moon in Pisces 23.43

# Reflections from January 2020

---------------------------------------------- Journaling & Notes ----------------------------------------------

Reflections from January 2020

------------------------------------------------ Journaling & Notes ------------------------------------------------

# Welcome to February 2020

## The Cards this Month

## 9th February – Full Moon Leo

At the time of this full Moon wonderfully expansive and forward-thinking Jupiter approaches Saturn and Pluto. This combination brings an amazing opportunity to rise above any petty ego concerns, to see the bigger picture, and expand our horizons.

Add to this, a powerful connection between Venus planet of love, balance and relational harmony, and Chiron, the planet of healing, both in Aries, the energy is with us to journey inwards, to cleanse and to rebalance. Use this time to notice any conflict between your ego self and your heart self. This full moon in Leo sits in the Mercury retrograde shadow so if you find yourself being wound up and irritated by others, try to stand back and recognize that they are on their own pathway of evolution, growth and learning. Thank them for the learning they have bought you and the contribution they have made in increasing your awareness and take the necessary steps to create firm boundaries that will hold you on your own pathway of spiritual development.

## 17th February – 10th March - Mercury Retrograde

When the winged messenger of the Gods slows down and appears to journey backwards, we are asked to do the same. Slow down. Do not be too attached to outcomes. Consider any obstacle that appears to stand in your way as a potential blessing in disguise. Look for the learning in every situation and center yourself in gratitude for all that you have right now. Be sure to back up your IT systems and if you are intending to travel, allow more time than usual.

## 23rd February – New Moon Pisces

The energy of the new Moon aligns with Mercury and Neptune and this powerful collaboration is also in harmony with Uranus, the planet of sudden change and dynamic Mars, the warrior planet, putting us in touch with our passions and desires. As the energy of Jupiter, Pluto and Saturn combine, in our ever-evolving process of manifestation, this powerful new Moon offers the perfect opportunity to set intentions to initiate changes to align our expanding vision for the future with our core inner values. With the Mercury retrograde energy at its peak, consider any sudden interruptions and diversions as signs from the universe bringing the opportunity to pause and to evaluate.

The Rune that spoke to us this month is Isa, the rune of standstill, withdrawal and ice. Beautifully aligning with the Mercury retrograde energy, this rune speaks of periods in time when events happen around us that can feel out of our control. Be patient, become an observer of yourself and use this time to meditate, cleanse and release.

Daydreams and Wishes for February 2020

---------------------------------------------- Journaling & Notes ----------------------------------------------

# Intentions for February 2020

---------------------------------------------- Journaling & Notes ----------------------------------------------

Journaling & Notes

27 Monday

Moon in Pisces

28 Tuesday

Moon in Pisces

29 Wednesday

Moon in Pisces – V/C 01.08 – Aries 11.50

30 Thursday

Moon in Aries

31 Friday

Moon in Aries – V/C 15.09

1 Saturday

Moon in Taurus 00.27

2 Sunday

Moon in Taurus 1.41 - First Quarter Moon - Imbolc/Lammas

------------------------------------------------ Journaling & Notes ------------------------------------------------

3 Monday

Moon in Taurus – V/C 11.27 – Moon in Gemini 11.28

4 Tuesday

Moon in Gemini

5 Wednesday

Moon in Gemini – V/C 14.19 – Cancer 19.02

6 Thursday

Moon in Cancer

7 Friday

Moon in Cancer – V/C 15.42 - Leo 22.44

8 Saturday

Moon in Leo

9 Sunday

Moon in Leo – Full Moon 07.33 – V/C 16.08 - Virgo 23.38

Journaling & Notes

## 10 Monday

Moon in Virgo

## 11 Tuesday

Moon in Virgo – V/C 18.25 - Libra 23.37

## 12 Wednesday

Moon in Libra

## 13 Thursday

Moon in Libra – V/C 21.40

## 14 Friday

Moon in Scorpio 00.37

## 15 Saturday

Moon in Scorpio – V/C 22.19 – Last Quarter Moon

## 16 Sunday

Moon in Sagittarius 04.06

February 2020

Journaling & Notes

## 17 Monday

Moon in Sagittarius - Mercury Retrograde until 10th March

## 18 Tuesday

Moon in Sagittarius – V/C 09.03 - Capricorn 10.36

## 19 Wednesday

Moon in Capricorn - Sun enters Pisces 04.56

## 20 Thursday

Moon in Capricorn – V/C 14.18 - Aquarius 19.41

## 21 Friday

Moon in Aquarius

## 22 Saturday

Moon in Aquarius – V/C 04.08

## 23 Sunday

Moon in Pisces 06.37 – New Moon 15.31

Reflections from February 2020

------------------------------------------------ Journaling & Notes ------------------------------------------------

## Reflections from February 2020

---------------------------------------------- Journaling & Notes ----------------------------------------------

# Welcome to March 2020

## The Cards this Month

9th March - Super Full Moon in Virgo

The super full moon in Virgo connects beautifully with Neptune opening channels for illumination and intuition, which in turn aligns with Saturn, Pluto, Jupiter and Mars, all in Capricorn, wow! Throw into this dynamic the meeting of Uranus, the great awakening and Venus, the planet of love and harmony and we can begin to see how powerful the energy around this full moon will be.

If you feel as though you would like to spring clean any aspect of your life, these connections bring you an opportunity to do exactly this. Mercury in retrograde can often bring elements of our past to our attention, particularly those that need adjusting. As we come to the end of this cycle and enter the shadow period, any aspects of our lives that have called for our attention can be attended to with the meticulous dedication of the nurturing energy of Virgo, before engaging with the energetic shift and heightened awareness of the Equinox.

10th March – Mercury Stations Direct

20th March - Equinox

If you are in the northern hemisphere this will be the spring equinox and if you are in the southern hemisphere autumn equinox.

What an extraordinary collaboration of energy to tap into and align with on our journey of manifestation. A time of energetic Fen Shui, as the earth pauses to breathe and Mercury stations direct, use this time of heightened awareness to prepare for fresh new beginnings.

The Rune that presented itself to us for March, is the rune of Dagaz this rune speaks of breakthrough and transformation. Still flavored by the energy of the Mercury retrograde, as we move into its shadow period and the energy of interruption dissipates, this rune often signals a major shift or breakthrough, sometimes resulting in a radical 180° change of direction.

Whilst such drastic changes may not be on your personal horizons, any shakeups in any areas of your life during the Mercury retrograde period can be processed at this time and integrated into any new beginnings that you wish to initiate at the time of the new moon in Aries...

24th March - New Moon Aries

This new Moon represents the beginning of a new astrological year and offers us brilliant opportunities to initiate new beginnings. If any of our New Year intentions that we made in January feel as though they have gone by the wayside, the combined energy of the equinox and the new Moon brings us the perfect opportunity to re-focus and get back on track.

In your personal journey of manifestation, working with the energies during March brings a period of cleansing and release. Use the Aries new Moon influence to its fullest, in sewing new seeds and beginning a new chapter of your journey in whatever context is relevant to your personal circumstances.

29th March – 6th April – Jupiter conjunct Pluto

This extraordinarily powerful connection only happens once every 12 years. In our journey of manifestation, the energy of this union lends itself to the initiation of any form of transformation that we wish to make that leads to the opening of new horizons and expanded opportunities.

## Intentions for March 2020

------------------------------------------------ Journaling & Notes ------------------------------------------------

Journaling & Notes

## 24 Monday

Moon in Pisces

## 25 Tuesday

Moon in Pisces – V/C 14.11 - Aries 18.47

## 26 Wednesday

Moon in Aries

## 27 Thursday

Moon in Aries

## 28 Friday

Moon in Aries – V/C 03.24 - Taurus 07.29

## 29 Saturday

Moon in Taurus

## 1 Sunday

Moon in Taurus – V/C 15.52 - Gemini 19.20

Journaling & Notes

## 2 Monday

Moon in Gemini – First Quarter Moon 19.57

## 3 Tuesday

Moon in Gemini

## 4 Wednesday

Moon in Gemini – V/C 02.19 - Cancer 04.25

## 5 Thursday

Moon in Cancer

## 6 Friday

Moon in Cancer – V/C 07.11 – Leo 09.27

## 7 Saturday

Moon in Leo

## 8 Sunday

Moon in Leo – V/C 08.12 – Virgo 10.47

Journaling & Notes

## 9 Monday

Moon in Virgo – Full Moon 17.47

## 10 Tuesday

Moon in Virgo – V/C 08.32 - Libra 10.02 – Mercury stations Direct 03.48

## 11 Wednesday

Moon in Libra

## 12 Thursday

Moon in Libra – V/C 08.11 - Scorpio 09.28

## 13 Friday

Moon in Scorpio

## 14 Saturday

Moon in Scorpio – V/C 10.05 – Sagittarius 11.09

## 15 Sunday

Moon in Sagittarius

Journaling & Notes

## 16 Monday

Moon in Sagittarius – V/C 09.34 – Capricorn 16.25 – Last Quarter Moon

## 17 Tuesday

Moon in Capricorn

## 18 Wednesday

Moon in Capricorn

## 19 Thursday

Moon in Capricorn – V/C 00.47 – Aquarius 01.15

## 20 Friday

Moon in Aquarius – V/C 08.59 – Equinox – Sun enters Aries 03.49

## 21 Saturday

Moon in Pisces 12.33

## 22 Sunday

Moon in Pisces

March 2020

Journaling & Notes

23 Monday

Moon in Pisces – V/C 14.51

24 Tuesday

Moon in Aries 00.57 – New Moon 09.28

25 Wednesday

Moon in Aries

26 Thursday

Moon in Aries – V/C 07.16 – Taurus 13.36

27 Friday

Moon in Taurus

28 Saturday

Moon in Taurus – V/C 23.04

29 Sunday

Moon in Gemini 02.37 – UK clocks go forward

Journaling & Notes

Journaling & Notes

# Welcome to April 2020

## The Cards this Month

29th March – 6th April – Jupiter conjunct Pluto

This once in every 12 years connection radiates the er
and liberation and will continue to flavor the resonar
from other planetary influences as we move into the
moon in Libra...

8th April – Super Full Moon Libra

We begin April with Mercury moving full steam ahead. As the
messenger passes by Neptune, the energy offers us potential for insightful conversations and illuminating communication. The energy of the super full moon calls us to find balance and harmony and in collaboration with the energy of Pluto, Jupiter and Saturn, who are linking harmoniously with Venus, currently travelling through Pisces, any discords or difficulties in relationships can be smoothed over and understood from a balanced perspective.

This is the perfect moon to engage in ceremonies of forgiveness, of both ourselves and others.

23rd April - New Moon Taurus

This new moon aligns with Uranus, the great awakener, who in turn, squares with Jupiter, Pluto and Saturn, suggesting the potential for sudden and unexpected changes, particularly in any areas of our lives which have been calling for regeneration, renewal and restructure.

Balanced by the grounding, earthy energy of Taurus we are invited to align with the natural rhythms of the universe. The energy of this new moon invites you to trust that if something in your life appears to be calling for change at this time, it will be opening new avenues of possibility that enlarge your horizons, bringing new hope, new optimism and new opportunity.

For anyone actively involved in manifestation this energy can free up any areas of blockage, particularly in our attitudes and perceptions to money and finance, generating changes that initiate new freedom and new opportunities.

The Rune that calls for our attention this month is Perth, the Rune of initiation. Rather like a rite of passage, this rune speaks of powerful changes taking place, often behind-the-scenes, with the universe calling us to trust and immerse ourselves in our personal journey of spiritual change and transformation. On occasions, the energy of this rune brings unexpected surprises and rewards and is symbolized by the flight of the Eagle, who free of the restrictions of everyday life, is able to unify with a higher vision.

# Inspiration and Desires for April 2020

---------------------------------------- Journaling & Notes ----------------------------------------

# Intentions for April 2020

------------------------------------------------ Journaling & Notes ------------------------------------------------

------------------------------------------------ Journaling & Notes ------------------------------------------------

30 Monday

Moon in Gemini – V/C 16.10

31 Tuesday

Moon in Cancer 12.43

1 Wednesday

Moon in Cancer – First Quarter Moon

2 Thursday

Moon in Cancer – V/C 17.48 – Leo 19.26

3 Friday

Moon in Leo – V/C 20.28

4 Saturday

Moon in Virgo 22.18

5 Sunday

Moon in Virgo

----------------------------------------------- Journaling & Notes -----------------------------------------------

## 6 Monday

Moon in Virgo – V/C 14.28 – Libra 22.16

## 7 Tuesday

Moon in Libra

## 8 Wednesday

Moon in Libra – Full Moon 03.34 – V/C 13.49 – Scorpio 21.16

## 9 Thursday

Moon in Scorpio

## 10 Friday

Moon in Scorpio – V/C 20.34 – Sagittarius 21.35 – Good Friday

## 11 Saturday

Moon in Sagittarius

## 12 Sunday

Moon in Sagittarius – V/C 12.45

------------------------------------------------ Journaling & Notes ------------------------------------------------

## 13 Monday

Moon in Capricorn 01.05 – Easter Monday

## 14 Tuesday

Moon in Capricorn – Last Quarter Moon

## 15 Wednesday

Moon in Capricorn – V/C 00.47 – Aquarius 08.36

## 16 Thursday

Moon in Aquarius

## 17 Friday

Moon in Aquarius – V/C 15.37 – Pisces 19.29

## 18 Saturday

Moon in Pisces

## 19 Sunday

Moon in Pisces – Sun enters Taurus 15.45

Journaling & Notes

## 20 Monday

Moon in Pisces – V/C00.30 – Aries 08.00

## 21 Tuesday

Moon in Aries

## 22 Wednesday

Moon in Aries – V/C 13.31 – Taurus 20.35

## 23 Thursday

Moon in Taurus – New Moon 03.25

## 24 Friday

Moon in Taurus

## 25 Saturday

Moon in Taurus – V/C 01.42 – Gemini 08.19

## 26 Sunday

Moon in Gemini

---------------------------------------------- Journaling & Notes ----------------------------------------------

Reflections from April 2020

------------------------------------------------ Journaling & Notes ------------------------------------------------

# Welcome to May 2020

## The Cards this Month

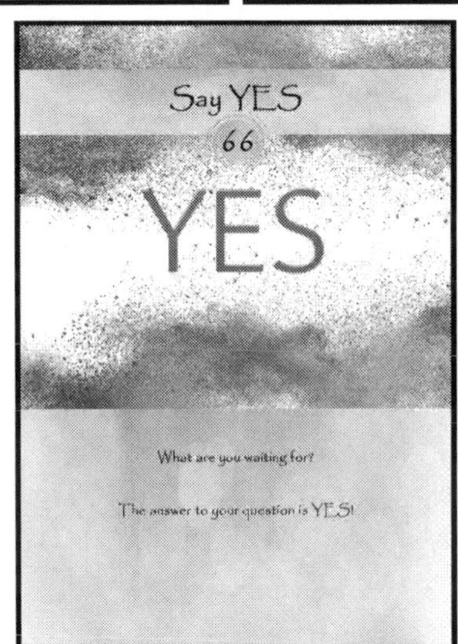

### 7th May – Full Moon Scorpio

Still flavored by the Uranus, Jupiter, Saturn and Pluto connection, offering the possibility of the kind of changes that inspire the expansion of our horizons, this full Moon invites us to dive deep and explore the depths of our unconscious. With lovely lunations between Neptune and Mercury, the planet of communication, plus Pluto moving into a retrograde position, this is a great time to journey inwards in search of insight and inspiration.

Enter your own dreamtime and allow your mind to wander. The dynamic energy of the masculine warrior planet Mars in Aquarius fuels our desires to bring about a higher vision for humanity, and with his passion beautifully softened by the feminine warrior planet Venus in Gemini the energy supports us in sharing our insights and awareness with others, collaborating for the greater collective.

### 13th May – 25th June – Venus Retrograde

Venus in retrograde offers us a time for reflection with an invitation to rebalance any aspects of our lives that are not in alignment with our core inner values.

### 22nd May – New Moon Gemini

At the time of this new moon, Venus is joined by Mercury, the winged messenger of the gods and the great communicator and bringer of wisdom. At the time of the new moon this partnership makes a powerful connection with Neptune. How this energy will affect us will to a very great extent depend on our individual personal circumstances. We might receive bucket loads of insight and illumination… or… we could find ourselves feeling rather confused, a little overwhelmed, unanchored and out at sea.

An ideal way to channel this kind of energy is to focus inwards. Rather than trying to strive ahead, in terms of manifestation, this energy offers us the perfect time to evaluate whether our external desires are in alignment with our core inner values. Jupiter, Pluto and Saturn, all now sit in a retrograde position and with gorgeous connections to this new moon, support us in identifying any changes that we wish to make, particularly in our communications with others.

The Runic guidance brought to us this month comes from the Rune of Jera. This is the rune of harvest, who speaks of a fertile season and a cycle of time, often spanning one year. Although this rune promises beneficial outcomes, it also advises us that we cannot rush things. Once we have sown seeds, even when they begin to sprout, we cannot force them to grow any faster. All we can do is provide them with the best conditions, offer them nurture and care, and be prepared to commit to the work involved to bring about a successful harvest.

Be sure to apply these principles, not only in your physical actions of manifestation but also in your words and in your communications with others. Remember we are all at different stages of our journey, each of us on our own individual pathways of learning. Observe every situation through the eyes of compassion...and that includes the way that you observe, relate and communicate with yourself!

## Intentions for May 2020

--------------------------------------------- Journaling & Notes ---------------------------------------------

------------------------------------------------ Journaling & Notes ------------------------------------------------

## 27 Monday

Moon in Gemini – V/C 17.59 – Cancer 18.27

## 28 Tuesday

Moon in Cancer

## 29 Wednesday

Moon in Cancer – V/C 20.29

## 30 Thursday

Moon in Leo 02.06 – First Quarter Moon

## 1 Friday

Moon in Leo – V/C 17.04 – Beltane/Samhain

## 2 Saturday

Moon in Virgo 06.35

## 3 Sunday

Moon in Virgo

Journaling & Notes

## 4 Monday

Moon in Virgo – V/C 03.24 – Libra 08.09 – UK Bank Holiday

## 5 Tuesday

Moon in Libra

## 6 Wednesday

Moon in Libra – V/C 03.30 – Scorpio 08.04

## 7 Thursday

Moon in Scorpio – Full Moon 11.45

## 8 Friday

Moon in Scorpio – V/C 03.38 – Sagittarius 08.15

## 9 Saturday

Moon in Sagittarius

## 10 Sunday

Moon in Sagittarius – V/C 07.10 – Capricorn 10.38

Journaling & Notes

## 11 Monday

Moon in Capricorn

## 12 Tuesday

Moon in Capricorn – V/C 11.29 - Aquarius 16.38

## 13 Wednesday

Moon in Aquarius – Venus Retrograde 07.44 until 25th June

## 14 Thursday

Moon in Aquarius – V/C 15.02 – Last Quarter Moon

## 15 Friday

Moon in Pisces 02.24

## 16 Saturday

Moon in Pisces

## 17 Sunday

Moon in Pisces – V/C 08.59 – Aries 14.35

May 2020

Journaling & Notes

## 18 Monday

Moon in Aries

## 19 Tuesday

Moon in Aries – V/C 21.32

## 20 Wednesday

Moon in Taurus 03.10 – Sun enters Gemini 14.49

## 21 Thursday

Moon in Taurus

## 22 Friday

Moon in Taurus – V/C 09.00 – Gemini 14.35 – New Moon 18.38

## 23 Saturday

Moon in Gemini

## 24 Sunday

Moon in Gemini – V/C 12.09

May 2020

Journaling & Notes

25 Monday

Moon in Cancer 00.08 – UK Bank Holiday

26 Tuesday

Moon in Cancer

27 Wednesday

Moon in Cancer – V/C 02.06 – Leo 07.32

28 Thursday

Moon in Leo – V/C 14.30

29 Friday

Moon in Virgo 12.40

30 Saturday

Moon in Virgo – First Quarter Moon

31 Sunday

Moon in Virgo – V/C 10.16 - Libra 15.37

## Reflections from May 2020

---------------------------------------------- Journaling & Notes ----------------------------------------------

# Reflections from May 2020

---------------------------------------------- Journaling & Notes ----------------------------------------------

# Welcome to June 2020

## The Cards this Month

If there was ever a month to take inspired action then this is it! Welcome to eclipse season and wow! What isn't happening this month!

The Rune that presented itself to us for the month of June is Ansuz, the messenger Rune, a rune of signals, signs, and synchronicities. The energy of this rune speaks of new and unexpected opportunities that call you into a new phase of your life. This rune invites us to be particularly aware of any information, communications, signs and signals that may be brought to us and to recognize them as guidance from the divine.

5th June – Full Moon Sagittarius – Lunar Eclipse

The empowered expansive energy of the full moon in Sagittarius, already intensified by the eclipse, finds an uneasy connection with Neptune and Mars and Venus and so we might expect emotions to run high, particularly in areas of relationship with any areas of dishonesty or disharmony coming to light.

However, with the energies of Jupiter, Pluto and Saturn still strongly connected, even if you find yourself facing a challenging situation, there will be purpose to this. Mercury, the planet of communication favors Uranus at this time and so channels for direct and realistic communication may suddenly open and with Venus still in retrograde we are invited to take our time, carefully review from all angles, being sure to take every perspective into account.

13th May – 25th June – Venus Retrograde

Listen to your heart, weigh things up and take time to evaluate. If you are called to stand your ground, connect with the lioness within and be true to your authentic self.

18th June – 12th July – Mercury Retrograde

The combination of Mercury in retrograde alongside eclipse season plus the energy surrounding the solstice, creates a kind of energetic portal that opens us to a timeline of increased awareness. During this period, we can receive clarity as to how events from the past have become interconnected with our thoughts, words and actions in the present, affecting the way in which we have been manifesting our future. A powerful time of insight and new awareness.

21st June – Solstice - New Moon Cancer – Solar Eclipse

With channels of energy open at their maximum during the phase of the solstice, this is a time of optimum potential to connect with the universe and not only receive guidance but also to set intentions to initiate steps that will support any new ideas into reality.

The wonderful nurturing energy of cancer supports us on our journey of manifestation those areas that affect the immediacy of our personal lives. Our homes, our families, our nearest and dearest and our communities and our tribe.

If all is going well on your journey of manifestation, new insights may come to you that propel your progress into the next phase of manifestation and if anything has been blocking your progress you may receive divine guidance requesting you to course correct or even to change direction completely. Either way, this energy often calls us to take action in real terms.

23rd June – 1st July – Jupiter conjunct Pluto

Over the coming months, the energy of this connection will increase and decrease in its intensity, eventually peaking in November. The joy of this expansive and transformative energy is that whatever changes we initiate during this time, as far as making conscious changes to our lives, this is a period when the energy of renewal and re-birth is 100% behind us.

## Intentions for June 2020

Journaling & Notes

## June 2020

------------------------------------------- Journaling & Notes -------------------------------------------

1 Monday

Moon in Libra

2 Tuesday

Moon in Libra – V/C 11.39 – Scorpio 17.05

3 Wednesday

Moon in Scorpio

4 Thursday

Moon in Scorpio – V/C 12.36 – Sagittarius 18.16

5 Friday

Moon in Sagittarius – Full Moon Eclipse 20.12

6 Saturday

Moon in Sagittarius – V/C 05.10 – Capricorn 20.44

7 Sunday

Moon in Capricorn

------------------------------------------------ Journaling & Notes ------------------------------------------------

## 8 Monday

Moon in Capricorn – V/C 19.05

## 9 Tuesday

Moon in Aquarius 01.53

## 10 Wednesday

Moon in Aquarius – V/C 15.34

## 11 Thursday

Moon in Pisces 10.31

## 12 Friday

Moon in Pisces

## 13 Saturday

Moon in Pisces – Last Quarter Moon 07.23 – V/C 13.44 – Aries 22.02

## 14 Sunday

Moon in Aries

June 2020

------------------------------------------------ Journaling & Notes ------------------------------------------------

## 15 Monday

Moon in Aries

## 16 Tuesday

Moon in Aries – V/C 01.49 – Taurus 10.35

## 17 Wednesday

Moon in Taurus

## 18 Thursday

Moon in Taurus – Mercury Retrograde 05.58 until 12th July – V/C 13.02 – Gemini 21.59

## 19 Friday

Moon in Gemini

## 20 Saturday

Moon in Gemini – Sun enters Cancer 22.43 – V/C 22.47 – Solstice northern hemisphere

## 21 Sunday

Moon in Cancer 07.01 – New Moon Eclipse 07.41 – Solstice southern hemisphere

---------------------------------------------- Journaling & Notes ----------------------------------------------

## 22 Monday

Moon in Cancer

## 23 Tuesday

Moon in Cancer – V/C 08.20 – Leo 13.33

## 24 Wednesday

Moon in Leo – V/C 06.34

## 25 Thursday

Moon in Virgo 18.04 – Venus stations Direct 07.48

## 26 Friday

Moon in Virgo

## 27 Saturday

Moon in Virgo – V/C 21.01 – Libra 21.16

## 28 Sunday

Moon in Libra – First Quarter Moon 09.15

## Reflections from June 2020

----------------------------------------------- Journaling & Notes -----------------------------------------------

Reflections from June 2020

---------------------------------------------- Journaling & Notes ----------------------------------------------

## Welcome to July 2020

The Cards this Month

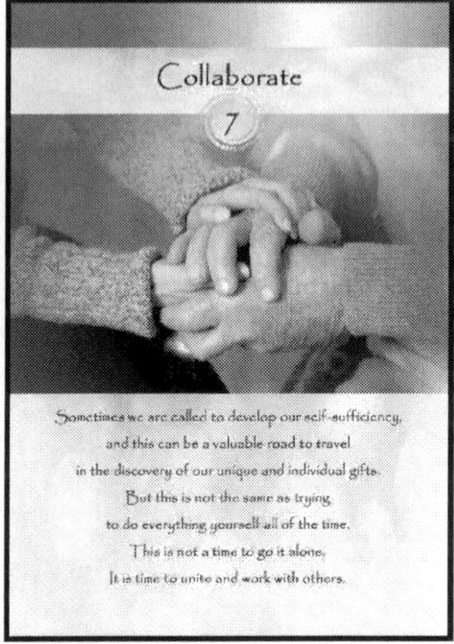

### 18th June – 12th July – Mercury Retrograde

The seemingly disruptive energy of Mercury in retrograde continues into July and in conjunction with eclipse season, the twisting and turning of the energy of this time, whilst potentially shaking us up, is actually calling for us to learn to live in attunement with the natural cycles of life and to recognize the part that we each play in co-creating our own life circumstances.

### 2nd July - Saturn re-enters Capricorn

Saturn, Father Time and the bringer of karmic lessons, now in retrograde, edges back towards Pluto and Jupiter, also in retrograde. The collective energetic ingredients of this collaboration invite us to lean into the learning of every situation that we encounter, observing ourselves through the lens of potential transformation.

### 5th July – Full Moon Capricorn - Lunar Eclipse

With the Sun and Mercury linked up in emotional Cancer, and the Moon, aligning in Capricorn with Jupiter, Pluto and Saturn all in retrograde, this looks to be an extraordinarily powerful eclipse. Add to this, the energy of the warrior planet Mars collaborating with Chiron the wounded healer, we can expect emotions and passions to run high.

The energy at this time often forces us to slow down, and to pay attention to any areas within ourselves that require healing. If you are a particularly sensitive person, during this time it is quite likely that you will pick up on the emotions and feelings of others. Be sure to set good boundaries and make space for alone time whenever you need it.

Favorable connections with Uranus, Neptune and Venus invite us to embrace any and all of our experiences during this time as opportunities sent to bring us insight and guidance.

### 12th July - Mercury Stations Direct

As Mercury stations direct and we enter what is known as the shadow period, the energy of the retrograde shifts and the winged messenger of the gods begins to move forwards again. During this phase the energy of disruption begins to realign inviting us to reflect and review the lessons brought to our attention during the retrograde period.

### 20th July - New Moon - Cancer

Given all of the work that has taken place on our pathway of manifestation during the eclipse season, and the lessons and reflections brought to us from the retrograde energies, with all of this growth and learning under our belts, we should be in a good position to understand any new directions that we wish to move towards and to be clear about the desires that we wish to manifest in real terms.

This is the second new moon of the year in cancer, which comes with a powerful and flowing connection to illuminating Neptune, inviting us to listen to our dreams. This is the perfect time to sit down and make a wish list.

The Rune that offered itself to us is Berkana, the rune of growth and rebirth. Symbolized by the Birch tree, this is a rune that speaks of new beginnings with the promise of a flourishing future.

Following a forest fire, the Birch tree is the very first tree to re-seed itself, and as such it represents the beginning of the potential for an entire new Forest to evolve and grow. The energy of this rune is profound and powerful, steady and consistent, and it brings an invitation for us to remove any form of resistance within ourselves, and to move forwards with the energy and vision of renewed hope.

# Intentions for July 2020

------------------------------------------- Journaling & Notes -------------------------------------------

Journaling & Notes

## June / July 2020

## 29 Monday

Moon in Libra – V/C 14.01 – Scorpio 23.47

## 30 Tuesday

Moon in Scorpio

## 1 Wednesday

Moon in Scorpio

## 2 Thursday

Moon in Scorpio – V/C 02.20 – Sagittarius 02.21

## 3 Friday

Moon in Sagittarius – V/C 14.05

## 4 Saturday

Moon in Capricorn 05.47

## 5 Sunday

Moon in Capricorn – Full Moon Eclipse 05.44

July 2020

Journaling & Notes

## 6 Monday

Moon in Capricorn – V/C 10.35 – Aquarius 11.08

## 7 Tuesday

Moon in Aquarius – V/C 05.37

## 8 Wednesday

Moon in Pisces 19.12

## 9 Thursday

Moon in Pisces

## 10 Friday

Moon in Pisces

## 11 Saturday

Moon in Pisces – V/C 04.48 – Aries 06.05

## 12 Sunday

Moon in Aries – Mercury stations Direct 09.26

July 2020

---------------------------------------------- Journaling & Notes ----------------------------------------------

## 13 Monday

Moon in Aries – Last Quarter Moon 00.28 - V/C 16.54 – Taurus 18.33

## 14 Tuesday

Moon in Taurus

## 15 Wednesday

Moon in Taurus

## 16 Thursday

Moon in Taurus – V/C 04.21 – Gemini 06.18

## 17 Friday

Moon in Gemini – V/C 22.14

## 18 Saturday

Moon in Cancer 15.23

## 19 Sunday

Moon in Cancer

Journaling & Notes

## 20 Monday

Moon in Cancer – New Moon 18.32 - V/C 18.54 – Leo 21.16

## 21 Tuesday

Moon in Leo

## 22 Wednesday

Moon in Leo – V/C 01.27 – Sun enters Leo 09.36

## 23 Thursday

Moon in Virgo 00.39

## 24 Friday

Moon in Virgo

## 25 Saturday

Moon in Virgo – V/C 00.07 – Libra 02.53

## 26 Sunday

Moon in Libra

# Reflections from July 2020

---------------------------------------------- Journaling & Notes ----------------------------------------------

## Reflections from July 2020

------------------------------------------------ Journaling & Notes ------------------------------------------------

# Welcome to August 2020

## The Cards this Month

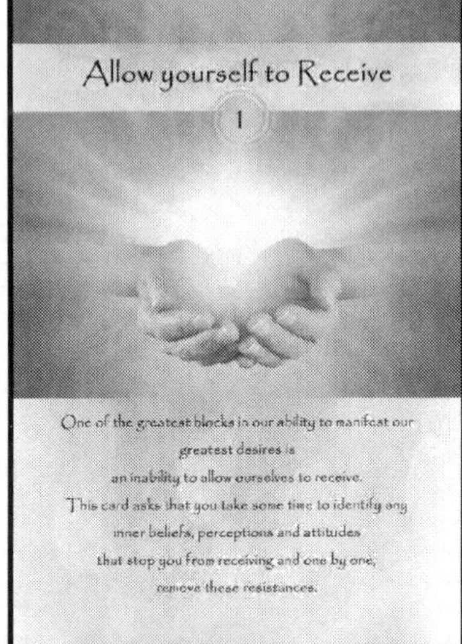


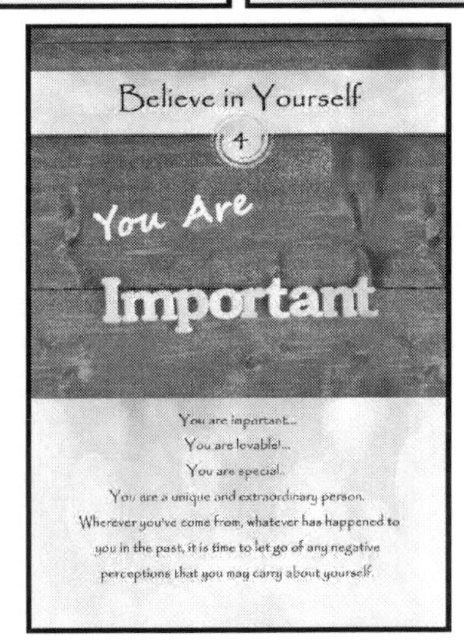

The governing energy of the Rune during August is the rune of Eihwaz, the rune of defense, symbolized by the Yew Tree.

This rune often appears at a time when we are beginning to forge new pathways in life, bringing with it an opportunity to identify the challenges that we inevitably face in the early stages of new beginnings. Beautifully in alignment with the incoming astrological energies this month, the energy of this rune advises patience and asks us not to try to force a situation into being.

The energy of this rune calls for integrity and compassion in all of our dealings.

## 3rd August – Full Moon – Aquarius

Every full moon offers us an opportunity to bring emotions to the surface and to release and to let go, energetically clearing the way for us to move forwards with our intentions, walking your talk and taking actions that are congruent with everything that we wish to manifest.

The energy of this full moon is particularly highly charged. With Jupiter, Pluto and Saturn all in retrograde, clashing with the energy of the warrior planet Mars, and Mercury, the planet of communication, we might expect some heated debates and passionate conversation! Add to this a full moon energy clash with Uranus the great awakener and things could get a little bit lively!

In terms of manifestation, consider this a period of time to engage in mindful observation, giving yourself plenty of opportunity for reflection and indeed permission NOT to react or to take any form of sudden action. Trust that the energy will shift as we move to the phase of the new Moon in Leo.

## 19th August – New Moon Leo

The new Moon in Leo is a wonderful time to embrace forgiveness, of both ourselves and others, and to clear the energy and make fresh new beginnings.

Although the warrior planet Mars is still linking in with Jupiter, Pluto and Saturn, his energy sits in a gorgeous alignment with the new Moon and Mercury, so if any words were spoken with haste, or sudden actions taken that we later regret, with Venus and Neptune in a beautifully flowing relationship with Saturn the energy is absolutely with us to hold open honest and frank discussions that move everything forwards harmoniously and in the best interests of all parties.

Surrounded by the lovely energy of Leo, we can each connect with the healthy attributes of pride that inspire us to step up into the very best version of ourselves. Become the hero or heroine of your own journey and renew your vows to walk a pathway of honor and integrity founded in strength of compassion.

Compassion literally means, com – passion… with passion. Speak from the heart and walk your truth but be sure to observe every situation through the eyes of love.

# Intentions for August 2020

------------------------------------------- Journaling & Notes -------------------------------------------

------------------------------------------------ Journaling & Notes ------------------------------------------------

## 27 Monday

Moon in Libra – V/C 02.08 – Scorpio 05.11 – First Quarter Moon 13.32

## 28 Tuesday

Moon in Scorpio

## 29 Wednesday

Moon in Scorpio – V/C 05.01 – Sagittarius 08.24

## 30 Thursday

Moon in Sagittarius

## 31 Friday

Moon in Sagittarius – V/C 01.07 – Capricorn 12.58

## 1 Saturday

Moon in Capricorn

## 2 Sunday

Moon in Capricorn – V/C 14.59 – Aquarius 19.10 – Lammas northern hemisphere

---------------------------------------------- Journaling & Notes ----------------------------------------------

## 3 Monday

Moon in Aquarius – Full Moon 16.58 – Imbolc southern hemisphere

## 4 Tuesday

Moon in Aquarius – V/C 22.45

## 5 Wednesday

Moon in Pisces 03.27

## 6 Thursday

Moon in Pisces

## 7 Friday

Moon in Pisces – V/C 13.53 – Aries 14.04

## 8 Saturday

Moon in Aries

## 9 Sunday

Moon in Aries – V/C 20.49

Journaling & Notes

## 10 Monday

Moon in Taurus 02.27

## 11 Tuesday

Moon in Taurus – Last Quarter Moon

## 12 Wednesday

Moon in Taurus – V/C 08.54 – Gemini 14.45

## 13 Thursday

Moon in Gemini

## 14 Friday

Moon in Gemini – V/C 12.19

## 15 Saturday

Moon in Cancer 00.35

## 16 Sunday

Moon in Cancer

------------------------------------------------ Journaling & Notes ------------------------------------------------

17 Monday

Moon in Cancer – V/C 00.58 – Leo 06.38

18 Tuesday

Moon in Leo

19 Wednesday

Moon in Leo – New Moon 03.41 - V/C 06.38 – Virgo 09.20

20 Thursday

Moon in Virgo

21 Friday

Moon in Virgo – V/C 04.36 – Libra 10.15

22 Saturday

Moon in Libra – Sun enters Virgo 16.44

23 Sunday

Moon in Libra – V/C 05.19 – Scorpio 11.15

August 2020

---------------------------------------------- Journaling & Notes ----------------------------------------------

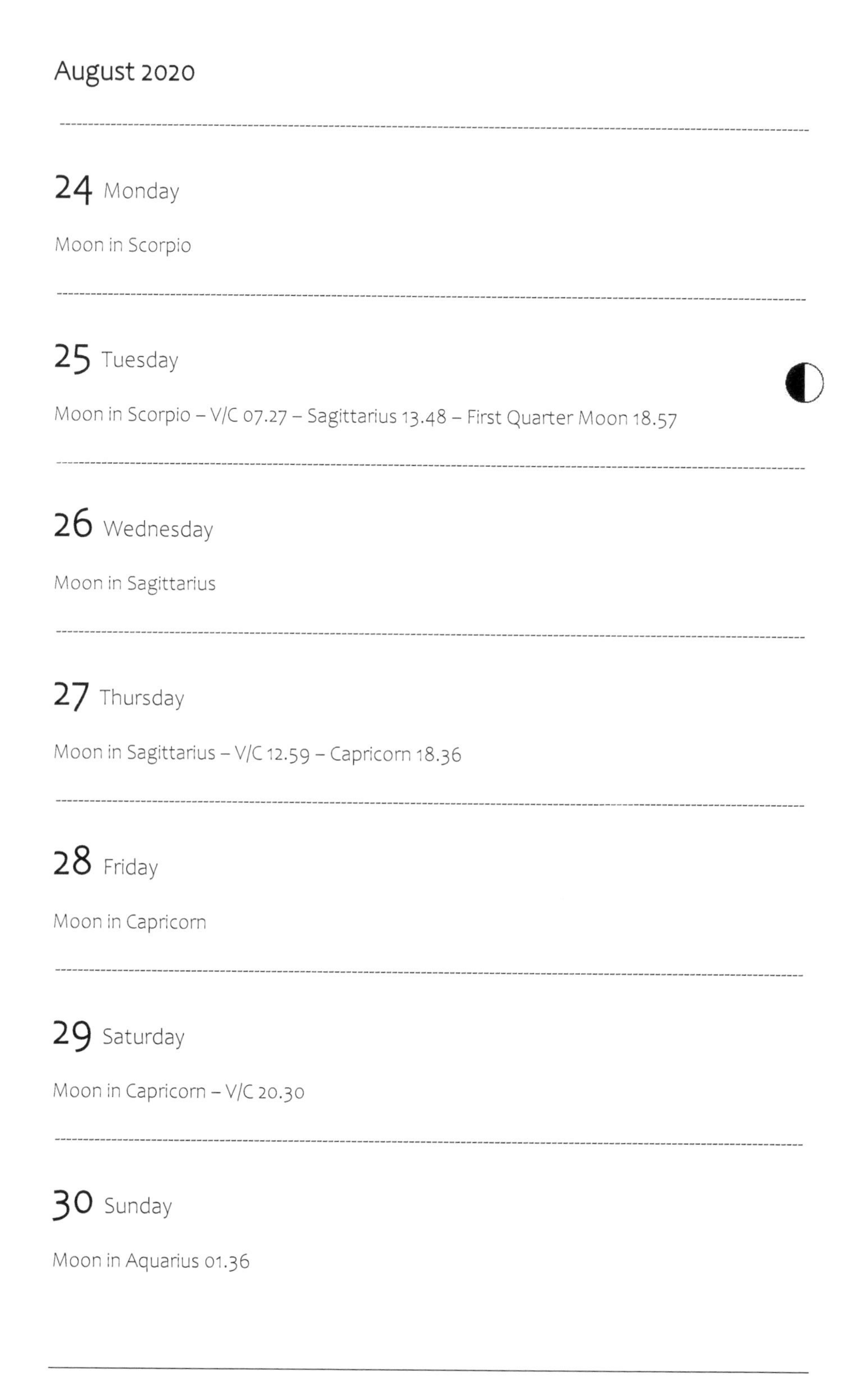

24 Monday

Moon in Scorpio

25 Tuesday

Moon in Scorpio – V/C 07.27 – Sagittarius 13.48 – First Quarter Moon 18.57

26 Wednesday

Moon in Sagittarius

27 Thursday

Moon in Sagittarius – V/C 12.59 – Capricorn 18.36

28 Friday

Moon in Capricorn

29 Saturday

Moon in Capricorn – V/C 20.30

30 Sunday

Moon in Aquarius 01.36

Reflections from August 2020

------------------------------------------------ Journaling & Notes ------------------------------------------------

Reflections from August 2020

---------------------------------------------- Journaling & Notes ----------------------------------------------

# Welcome to September 2020

## The Cards this Month

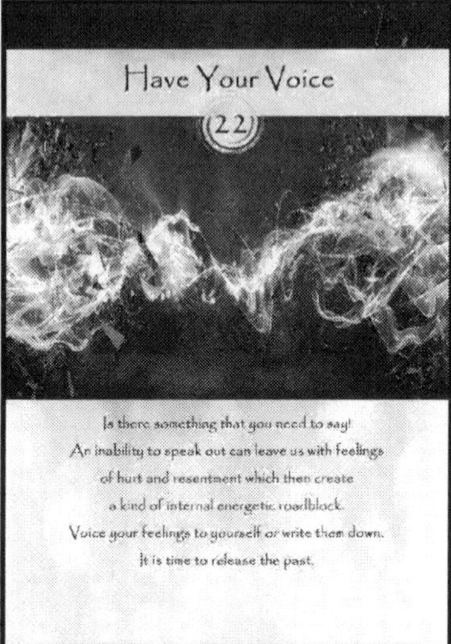

## 2nd September – Full Moon – Pisces

During September, the passionate and energetic warrior planet Mars, moves into retrograde. September also brings the Equinox, which in the northern hemisphere will be a turning to autumn, and in the southern hemisphere a turning to spring. In anticipation of these powerful energetic shifts, during the phase of the full Moon in Pisces we are presented with a wonderful opportunity to enter an internal space of reflection and evaluation in preparation for the next chapter of the year.

At the time of this full moon, we are gifted with a balance of both flowing energy as well as a little friction and I find myself reminded that the energy of friction can also give us traction. Knowing what we dislike helps us to adjust our course as much as knowing what we do like. The key of course is what we do in response to our experiences.

The energy at this time connects us with Thurisaz, the rune of Gateway. This rune invites us to imagine climbing to the top of a mountain, pausing to stand still, and to look back and reflect upon the journey that brought us to where we are right now, acknowledging the ups and the downs, the peaks and the troughs, and every experience that has brought us to this present moment and has contributed to the person that we have become today. We are invited to reflect and to review, and to offer appreciation for every aspect of our learning, the easy lessons and also those that were more challenging, before walking through the gateway and entering a new phase and chapter in our lives.

## 9th September – 14th November – Mars Retrograde

As the warrior planet pauses, and appears to travel backwards, take full advantage of this energy to integrate wisdom and learning with action. Mars in retrograde brings a wonderful opportunity to understand how our past experiences have influenced our responses and actions, and therefore impacted on our personal process of manifestation. In bringing the awareness of hindsight to our pathway of learning, the energy of Mars in retrograde is truly a gift for the spiritual Warrior.

## 17th September – New Moon – Virgo

With the energy of Jupiter stationed direct for the entire month of September and still connecting in with clear thinking Saturn and transformative Pluto, the new Moon in Virgo links with Neptune to make a stunning connection with this powerful trio.

Although there are some more strained connections between Venus, the planet of harmony, and Uranus, the great awakener, with Mercury and Mars in retrograde also having a say, the overall energy offers us an ideal time to literally get our act together.

Sometimes setting intentions involves entering a space of dreamtime, however the energy of this new moon is all about doing and taking action. On our journey of conscious manifestation, this is the perfect time to draw up lists and make a firm commitment to putting them into action. And although the energies are quite intense, details that really do need to be attended to can be identified, and with hindsight and self-reflection, solutions can be sought, and ways forwards planned.

22nd September – Equinox – Sun enters Libra

In this portal of opportunity, the astrological collaborations at this time offer an extraordinary opportunity to gain clarity through self-reflection. Take time to evaluate and really ask yourself if your actions in the world are congruent with everything that you wish to see.

Still drawing on the energy of the new Moon in Virgo, during the four days that surround the Equinox the incoming energy invites us to make a firm commitment to walking our talk and to ‘being’ the change that we wish to see in the world.

## Intentions for September 2020

---------------------------------------------- Journaling & Notes ----------------------------------------------

------------------------------------------------ Journaling & Notes ------------------------------------------------

31 Monday

Moon in Aquarius – UK Bank Holiday

1 Tuesday

Moon in Aquarius – V/C 05.56 – Pisces 10.34

2 Wednesday

Moon in Pisces – Full Moon 06.21

3 Thursday

Moon in Pisces – V/C 15.34 – Aries 21.21

4 Friday

Moon in Aries

5 Saturday

Moon in Aries

6 Sunday

Moon in Aries – V/C 05.44 – Taurus 09.43

## September 2020

---------------------------------------------- Journaling & Notes ----------------------------------------------

7 Monday

Moon in Taurus

8 Tuesday

Moon in Taurus – V/C 13.46 – Gemini 22.27

9 Wednesday

Moon in Gemini – Mars Retrograde until 14th November 23.22

10 Thursday

Moon in Gemini – Last Quarter Moon

11 Friday

Moon in Gemini – V/C 05.47 – Cancer 09.22

12 Saturday

Moon in Cancer

13 Sunday

Moon in Cancer – V/C 13.04 – Leo 16.32

---------------------------------------------- Journaling & Notes ----------------------------------------------

## 14 Monday

Moon in Leo

## 15 Tuesday

Moon in Leo – V/C 16.09 – Virgo 19.37

## 16 Wednesday

Moon in Virgo

## 17 Thursday

Moon in Virgo - New Moon 12.00 – V/C 12.41 – Libra 19.55

## 18 Friday

Moon in Libra

## 19 Saturday

Moon in Libra – V/C 15.28 – Scorpio 19.32

## 20 Sunday

Moon in Scorpio

## September 2020

---------------------------------------------- Journaling & Notes ----------------------------------------------

## 21 Monday

Moon in Scorpio – V/C 19.12 – Sagittarius 20.31

## 22 Tuesday

Moon in Sagittarius – Sun enters Libra 14.30 – Autumn Equinox northern hemisphere

## 23 Wednesday

Moon in Sagittarius – V/C 18.31 – Autumn Equinox southern hemisphere

## 24 Thursday

Moon in Capricorn 00.16 – First Quarter Moon

## 25 Friday

Moon in Capricorn

## 26 Saturday

Moon in Capricorn – V/C 04.35 – Aquarius 07.07

## 27 Sunday

Moon in Aquarius

------------------------------------------- Journaling & Notes -------------------------------------------

## Reflections from September 2020

------------------------------------------------ Journaling & Notes ------------------------------------------------

# Welcome to October 2020

## The Cards this Month

### 9th September – 14th November – Mars Retrograde

With Mars in retrograde for the entire month of October, in any situation where passions run high, be sure to stand back and evaluate, giving yourself opportunity to hold the perspective of the bigger picture, before speaking your mind, making decisions, and taking action.

### 1st October – Full Moon – Aries

The energy of this full moon speaks of both healing and wounding. The moon pairs up with the energy of Chiron, the wounded healer, with some pressure applied to them from Saturn, Father Time and the planet of karma. which is in turn influenced by the illumination of Neptune. Add to this, the Pluto, Jupiter, Saturn collaboration making a strong connection with Mars in retrograde, this looks to be a dynamic and powerful period.

During this phase of the moon consider any challenges that arise as an opportunity to heal. In every situation that we face, we always have a choice as to how we respond. Learning to release emotional tension clears the way for mindful thinking, enabling us to step into a position of empowerment, underpinned by awareness of both ourselves and others. This is an excellent moon to release any emotional residue from the past, and to seek healing through awareness.

### 14th October – 3rd November - Mercury Retrograde

Be sure to backup your IT systems, and lean into the possibility of diversions, interruptions and delays, in the knowledge that the universe will always have the upper hand, and sometimes demands that we slow down the pace, detach ourselves from our perceived goals, and trust that way is being shown.

### 16th October – Super New Moon - Libra

The energy of the super new moon in Libra invites us to better and improve all of our relationships. This is a time when we can tap into the illumination of Neptune and invest in the process of visioning in kinds of relationships that we desire, not only for ourselves individually, but for all of humanity. This phase of the moon offers us the opportunity to dream ourselves into relationships of equality, fluent in effective, emotionally aware communication.

At this time, any issues that surface in connection to relationships are presenting themselves as an opportunity for change. If you are single and find yourself yearning for a relationship, then please listen to your desires and take them seriously. If you are seeking your soulmate, this is an ideal time to create a vision board that focuses on the qualities of relationship that you desire.

Likewise, if you are in an existing relationship, the energy at this time invites you to invest in strengthening this commitment. Relationships can so easily fall into comfortable patterns, where we forget to let our love ones know how much we really care about them. The energy of this new moon invites us to affirm these connections and to let people know how we really feel.

31st October – Full Moon - Taurus

Northern hemisphere, Festival of Samhain. Southern hemisphere, Festival of Beltane.

Directly aligning with the great awakener and bringer of sudden changes, Uranus, the energy of this moon promises to be intense, exciting and potentially changeable, and aligns beautifully with the energy of the Rune of Hagalaz. Rather like the planet of Uranus, this rune is known as the great awakener. Bringing the energy of disruption, it calls for change, freedom and liberation and when we draw this rune in a reading, it is an acknowledgement that when sudden happenings occur, the changes are timely and appropriate for our personal growth and that the universe and our soul are calling for change.

In Celtic and pagan traditions, the festival of Samhain marked the beginning of a New Year, a whole new cycle of growth, and so the energy at this time invites us to recognize any areas of our lives that we have outgrown.

With the energy of Jupiter, Pluto and Saturn, bringing powerful opportunity for realistic, empowered and expansive transformation, making connections with Mars and Mercury, both in retrograde, we must trust that any interruptions and diversions to our pathway at this time, will be opening much-needed new avenues of possibility for us.

## Intentions for October 2020

---------------------------------------------- Journaling & Notes ----------------------------------------------

Journaling & Notes

## 28 Monday

Moon in Aquarius – V/C 08.17 – Pisces 16.33

## 29 Tuesday

Moon in Pisces

## 30 Wednesday

Moon in Pisces – V/C 18.29

## 1 Thursday

Moon in Aries 03.46 – Full Moon 22.05

## 2 Friday

Moon in Aries

## 3 Saturday

Moon in Aries – V/C 06.47 – Taurus 16.12

## 4 Sunday

Moon in Taurus

October 2020

---------------------------------------------- Journaling & Notes ----------------------------------------------

## 5 Monday

Moon in Taurus – V/C 19.40

## 6 Tuesday

Moon in Gemini 05.02

## 7 Wednesday

Moon in Gemini

## 8 Thursday

Moon in Gemini – V/C 02.56 – Cancer 16.45

## 9 Friday

Moon in Cancer

## 10 Saturday

Moon in Cancer – Last Quarter Moon 01.39 - V/C 17.03

## 11 Sunday

Moon in Leo 01.24

Journaling & Notes

## 12 Monday

Moon in Leo – V/C 15.29

## 13 Tuesday

Moon in Virgo 05.55

## 14 Wednesday

Moon in Virgo – V/C 23.46 – Mercury Retrograde until 3rd November 02.04

## 15 Thursday

Moon in Libra 06.53

## 16 Friday

Moon in Libra – V/C 23.11 – New Moon 20.30

## 17 Saturday

Moon in Scorpio 06.05

## 18 Sunday

Moon in Scorpio – V/C 22.42

Journaling & Notes

## 19 Monday

Moon in Sagittarius 05.42

## 20 Tuesday

Moon in Sagittarius

## 21 Wednesday

Moon in Sagittarius – V/C 04.37 – Capricorn 07.43

## 22 Thursday

Moon in Capricorn – Sun enters Scorpio 23.59

## 23 Friday

Moon in Capricorn – V/C 05.34 – Aquarius 13.16 – First Quarter Moon 14.22

## 24 Saturday

Moon in Aquarius – V/C 22.53

## 25 Sunday

Moon in Pisces 21.18 – UK clocks go back

Reflections from October 2020

---------------------------------------------- Journaling & Notes ----------------------------------------------

# Reflections from October 2020

Journaling & Notes

# Welcome to November 2020

## The Cards for this Month

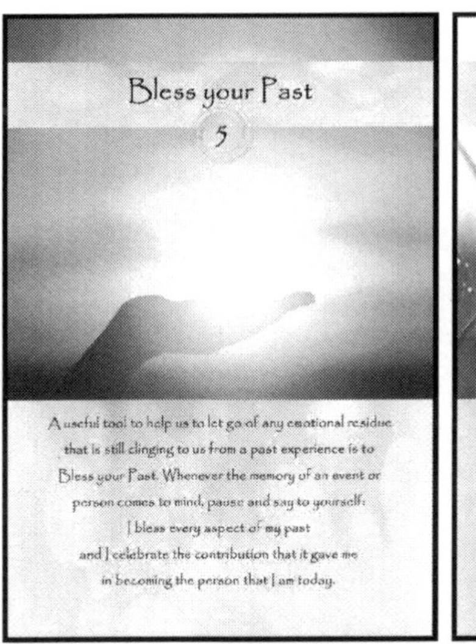

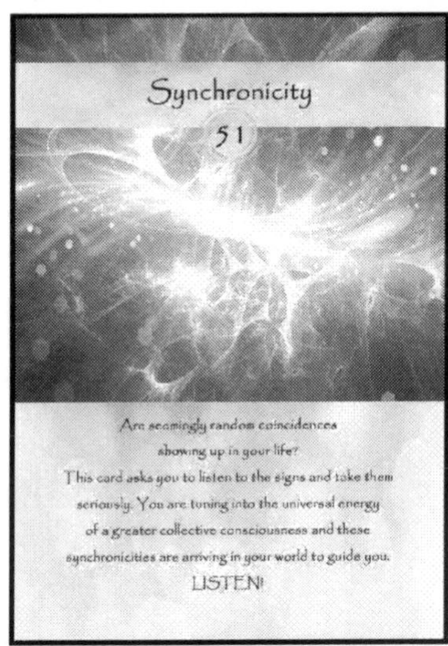

14th October – 3rd November Mercury Retrograde

As the retrograde period comes to an end, we will still feel the residue of this energy during the shadow period. This tends to last no more than two weeks and is a gradual fade out. Shadow periods invite us to reflect on any interruptions and delays and to consider the information that was brought to us during this time, offering us an opportunity to reflect and integrate this new awareness into our future plans.

9th September – 14th November - Mars Retrograde

As the warrior energy of Mars in retrograde comes to an end, in alignment with the Mercury retrograde shadow, be sure to integrate all of the learning brought to you over the course of this time. As we approach the super new Moon in Scorpio, we are invited to dive deep.

15th November - Super New Moon – Scorpio

The energy of this powerful super new moon invites us to journey into our unconscious and connect with our deepest desires, our hopes and our dreams. And as we integrate our learning from the retrograde planets into our full awareness, this phase of the moon brings an extraordinary opportunity to set our intentions to walk the pathway of conscious living and to align with the calling of the spiritual Warrior who sits within us all.

The Rune that shares its wisdom with us at this time is Raido, the rune of Journey. This rune inspires and draws us towards communication, union and reunion. Although the journey is usually one that takes us inwards, inviting a process of self-healing and self-change, creating an increase in our self-worth and self-esteem, the energy of this rune can also suggest a need for spiritual connection and communication. We are encouraged to reach out for guidance and support, particularly in areas of communication, especially those that support not only our own personal growth but our ability to share our insights and knowledge with others.

30th November – Full Moon Gemini - Lunar Eclipse

Welcome to eclipse season and what an extraordinary week we have with an abundance of dynamic energy available for us to process our thoughts and identify the difference between mindful thinking patterns that fuel our ability to live an empowered conscious life, and those thinking patterns that tend to be attached to perceptions and beliefs from the past.

Intensified and heightened by the energy of the eclipse this phase of the moon affords us the maximum opportunity to gain awareness of the way in which we communicate, not only with others but also within ourselves.

Are the words you use within your inner dialogue kind, caring and compassionate or are you harsh and judgmental of yourself in ways that undermine your own self-worth and self-esteem? Make a commitment to let go of inner criticism and change your inner critic into an inner critique who offers constructive feedback aimed to support your growth and bring out the very best of you.

# Intentions for November 2020

Journaling & Notes

Journaling & Notes

## 26 Monday

Moon in Pisces

## 27 Tuesday

Moon in Pisces

## 28 Wednesday

Moon in Pisces – V/C 00.45 – Aries 08.44

## 29 Thursday

Moon in Aries

## 30 Friday

Moon in Aries – V/C 16.12 – Taurus 21.18

## 31 Saturday

Moon in Taurus – Full Moon 14.49 –Samhain/Beltane

## 1 Sunday

Moon in Taurus

------------------------------------------------ Journaling & Notes ------------------------------------------------

## 2 Monday

Moon in Taurus – V/C 02.29 – Gemini 0 9.59

## 3 Tuesday

Moon in Gemini – Mercury stations Direct 17.49

## 4 Wednesday

Moon in Gemini – V/C 13.48 – Cancer 21.45

## 5 Thursday

Moon in Cancer

## 6 Friday

Moon in Cancer

## 7 Saturday

Moon in Cancer – V/C 01.26 – Leo 07.18

## 8 Sunday

Moon in Leo – Last Quarter Moon

November 2020

------------------------------------------------ Journaling & Notes ------------------------------------------------

## 9 Monday

Moon in Leo – V/C 11.04 – Virgo 13.29

## 10 Tuesday

Moon in Virgo

## 11 Wednesday

Moon in Virgo – V/C 10.58 – Libra 16.09

## 12 Thursday

Moon in Libra

## 13 Friday

Moon in Libra – V/C 11.32 – Scorpio 16.18

## 14 Saturday

Moon in Scorpio – Mars stations Direct 00.35

## 15 Sunday

Moon in Scorpio – New Moon 05.07 – V/C 11.12 – Sagittarius 15.46

Journaling & Notes

16 Monday

Moon in Sagittarius

17 Tuesday

Moon in Sagittarius – V/C 07.54 – Capricorn 16.34

18 Wednesday

Moon in Capricorn

19 Thursday

Moon in Capricorn – V/C 16.29 – Aquarius 20.24

20 Friday

Moon in Aquarius

21 Saturday

Moon in Aquarius – V/C 00.48 – Sun enters Sagittarius 20.39

22 Sunday

Moon in Pisces 04.05 – First Quarter Moon 04.44

Journaling & Notes

## 23 Monday

Moon in Pisces

## 24 Tuesday

Moon in Pisces – V/C 10.44 – Aries 15.04

## 25 Wednesday

Moon in Aries

## 26 Thursday

Moon in Aries – V/C 23.46

## 27 Friday

Moon in Taurus 03.42

## 28 Saturday

Moon in Taurus

## 29 Sunday

Moon in Taurus – V/C 12.48 – Gemini 16.15

Reflections from November 2020

---------------------------------------------- Journaling & Notes ----------------------------------------------

Reflections from November 2020

------------------------------------------------ Journaling & Notes ------------------------------------------------

# Welcome to December 2020

## The Cards this Month

14th December – New Moon Sagittarius – Solar Eclipse

At the time of this new moon eclipse, the gentle and harmonious energy of Venus is favoring the Jupiter, Saturn and Pluto alliance, and even though their energy in turn clashes with the warrior planet of Mars, this energy then flows beautifully to the new moon who is aligning with Mercury, the winged messenger of the gods and the planet of our developing wisdom.

Bring in the Sagittarius flavor of honesty and integrity and we can see that the dynamics available during this week will support any intentions that are founded in truth, fairness and justice. On our journey of manifestation, the energy at this time offers a fabulous opportunity to review our long-term visions and make plans for the future.

With Saturn approaching Aquarius, seem to be joined by Jupiter, this is an ideal opportunity to tune into higher visions and expansive new possibilities, especially if our thoughts and ideas are likely to lead us into new adventures and new territory.

18th December – Saturn moves into Aquarius
20th December – Jupiter moves into Aquarius
21st December - Solstice

If you haven't already done so, with both Saturn and Jupiter moving into Aquarius and aligning their energy with one another, this is an amazing week to set your New Year intentions…and dream big!

At the time of the solstice, when the Earth pauses for breath and the divide between worlds is thin, we can receive significant downloads of divine guidance and inspiration to support us on our journey of manifestation.

The rune associated with the overall energy of December is Odin, the blank rune, the All-Father, whose energy holds the potential of the unknowable and the divine. This rune is both an end and a beginning, and it invites us to immerse ourselves in complete trust. This blank rune indicates a time of gestation when new possibilities can be born and its energy represents the infinite source of potential that lies in the unknowable future.

Although uncertainties so often accompanies transition, causing us to wobble at such times, this rune of great power, also brings reassurance that we are progressing in our lives and changes are happening in support of the growth and evolution of our soul.

30th December – Full Moon Cancer

What a wonderful energy to send us into 2021.

As we prepare to embrace a New Year in our journey of manifestation with powerful and flowing connections with Uranus and Mercury this phase of the moon offers an extraordinary opportunity to re-align ourselves with new possibilities, leading to new directions and new purpose.

Although the energy of Neptune the great illuminator clashes with Venus during this phase of the moon, rest assured that any confusion you experience during this time is being brought to your attention with purpose, indeed confusion, is almost always an aspect of the journey that ultimately leads us into clarity.

The Jupiter Saturn conjunction in collaboration with Pluto and Mercury, calls us to listen. Softened by aspects to the moon, the energy of this time invites us to pause, to get still and center ourselves in a space of reverence. Within this space of possibility, offer prayers for the year that has passed while simultaneously reaching into your hopes and dreams for the coming year.

# Intentions for December 2020

Journaling & Notes

---------------------------------------------- Journaling & Notes ----------------------------------------------

## 30 Monday

○

Moon in Gemini – Full Moon Eclipse 09.29

## 1 Tuesday

Moon in Gemini – V/C 04.21

## 2 Wednesday

Moon in Cancer 03.32

## 3 Thursday

Moon in Cancer

## 4 Friday

Moon in Cancer – V/C 10.28 – Leo 12.52

## 5 Saturday

Moon in Leo – V/C 22.27

## 6 Sunday

Moon in Virgo 19.46

December 2020

---------------------------------------------- Journaling & Notes ----------------------------------------------

## 7 Monday

Moon in Virgo

## 8 Tuesday

Moon in Virgo – Last Quarter Moon 00.36 – V/C 22.35

## 9 Wednesday

Moon in Libra 00.01

## 10 Thursday

Moon in Libra

## 11 Friday

Moon in Libra – V/C 00.56 – Scorpio 01.58

## 12 Saturday

Moon in Scorpio

## 13 Sunday

Moon in Scorpio – V/C 01.57 – Sagittarius 02.39

------------------------------------------- Journaling & Notes -------------------------------------------

## 14 Monday

Moon in Sagittarius – V/C 16.16 – New Moon Eclipse 16.16

## 15 Tuesday

Moon in Capricorn 03.34

## 16 Wednesday

Moon in Capricorn

## 17 Thursday

Moon in Capricorn – V/C 05.34 – Aquarius 06.26

## 18 Friday

Moon in Aquarius

## 19 Saturday

Moon in Aquarius – V/C 08.44 – Pisces 12.38

## 20 Sunday

Moon in Pisces

December 2020

---------------------------------------------- Journaling & Notes ----------------------------------------------

## 21 Monday

Moon in Pisces – Sun enters Capricorn 10.02 – V/C 10.24 – Aries 22.32 – Solstice
First Quarter Moon 23.41

## 22 Tuesday

Moon in Aries

## 23 Wednesday

Moon in Aries – V/C 22.50

## 24 Thursday

Moon in Taurus 10.55 – Christmas Eve

## 25 Friday

Moon in Taurus – Christmas Day

## 26 Saturday

Moon in Taurus – V/C 11.31 – Gemini 23.32 – Boxing Day

## 27 Sunday

Moon in Gemini

Journaling & Notes

## 28 Monday

Moon in Gemini – UK Bank Holiday

## 29 Tuesday

Moon in Gemini – V/C 03.00 – Cancer 10.28

## 30 Wednesday

Moon in Cancer – Full Moon 03.28

## 31 Thursday

Moon in Cancer – V/C 13.44 – Leo 18.57 – New Year's Eve

## 1 Friday

Moon in Leo – New Year's Day

## 2 Saturday

Moon in Leo – V/C 21.59

## 3 Sunday

Moon in Virgo 01.12

Journaling & Notes

Reflections from December 2020

------------------------------------------------ Journaling & Notes ------------------------------------------------

# Additional Notes

------------------------------------------------ Journaling & Notes ------------------------------------------------

## Additional Notes

------------------------------------------------ Journaling & Notes ------------------------------------------------

# Welcome to 2021

## Cards of Promise for the Coming Year

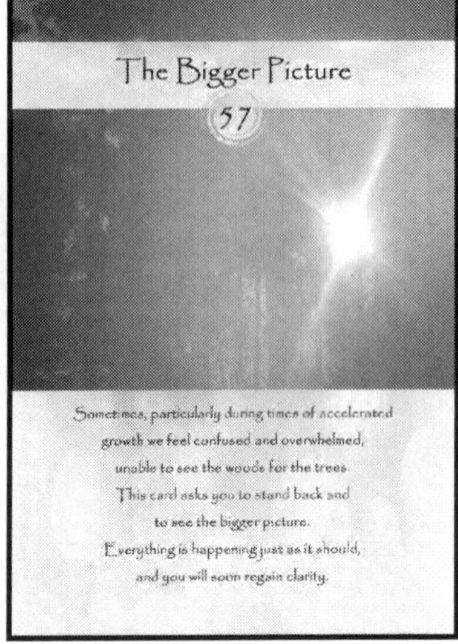

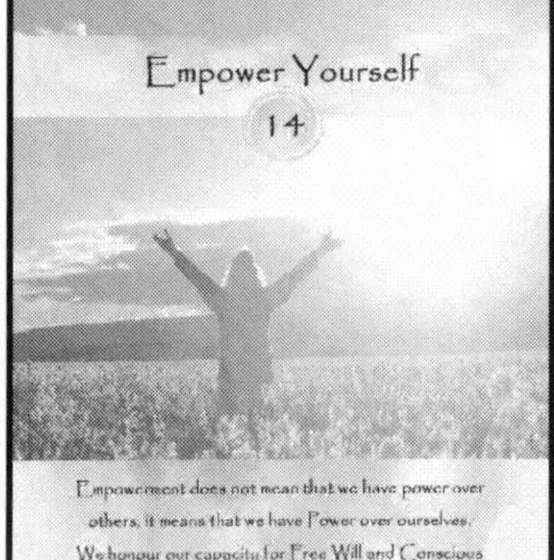

Journaling & Notes

The Art of Manifestation Oracle Cards

To find out more about the 'I Choose Love' series, including the Oracle Cards that are featured in this diary, visit the Card and Book Page in the A-Z of Emotional Heath FREE online Library.

www.azemotionalheath.com/bookscards

## About the Author

Jenny Florence worked as an Accredited BACP, UKRC Registered Counsellor for over 26 years. She has written several books including 7 Steps to Spiritual Empathy, Mindfulness meets Emotional Awareness, 7 Steps to Learn the Language of your Emotions and the I Choose Love Series which includes the Art of Manifestation Oracle Cards. She first began reading Runes and Tarot cards as a teenager and has also studied Astrology.

She is the founder and creator of the A-Z of Emotional Health on-line Video Library, a free Public Resource, understanding Emotional and Mental Wellness from a holistic perspective.

https://www.azemotionalhealth.com/

You can also follow her on Social Media

Youtube – AZEmotionalHealth

Facebook - https://www.facebook.com/azofemotionalhealth/

Made in the USA
San Bernardino, CA
17 December 2019